3.00

OC

SEP

MAR 2

FAIRY ELVES

A dictionary of the little people
with some old tales and verses about them

Robin Palmer and Pelagie Doane

New York   Henry Z. Walck, Inc.   *1964*

Fairy elves,
Whose midnight revels, by a forest side
Or fountain some belated peasant sees,
Or dreams he sees, while overhead the moon
Sits arbitress.

John Milton, PARADISE LOST

Library of Congress Catalog Card Number: 64–21123

PRINTED IN THE UNITED STATES OF AMERICA

Acknowledgments

Grateful appreciation is given to the following publishers and copyright holders for permission to use the selections listed.

Appleton-Century-Crofts and the *St. Nicholas Magazine* for permission to use "The Little Elf" by John Kendrick Bangs.

Little, Brown & Co. for permission to use "Will-o'-the-Wisp" from *Tirra Lirra* by Laura E. Richards.

Mrs. Harold Monro for permission to use "Overheard on a Salt Marsh" by Harold Monro.

Frederick Warne & Co. for permission to use part of "The Honey Feast" from *The Dumas Fairy Tale Book* by Alexandre Dumas.

Elizabeth Yates for permission to use "The Piskey Revelers" from *Piskey Folk* by Enys Tregarthen, collected by Elizabeth Yates. Copyright 1940 by Elizabeth Yates.

Contents

Fairy Dictionary

Since fairies have the gift of flight, though not necessarily by means of wings, it is not surprising that the same ones turn up again and again in different countries. Sometimes they change their names or the spelling of them as they hop across the North Sea or the English Channel, but they behave very much as they did before. So the Brownie of Britain is the Kobold of Germany or the Nis of the Scandinavian countries. In the following pages you will find descriptions of many fairy people and some of the old folk tales that are told about them.

BOGGART   Great Britain

The boggart is the tiniest of fairies, barely half as long as your thumb. He lives in a knothole and is always teasing children and annoying grown-ups; but no one ever sees him. If you happen to poke a pencil or a little stick into his house when he is at home, he will send it shooting back at you. One of his bad habits is to move things about so that they trip people who get out of bed in the dark.

BROWNIE   Great Britain

Lucky is the housewife who has a brownie in her cellar! He will often help her with her work and all he asks in return is a bowl of fresh milk left behind the door at bedtime. Brownies look like little old men with wrinkled faces. They have short, curly hair and wear brown suits. Often they are mischievous and play tricks, especially on people who are unkind or lazy. In Scotland they are said to dislike any form of waste and never fail to punish those who are not thrifty.

CHANGELING   Most of Europe

Sometimes the fairies take a human baby and leave one of their own in the cradle. This fairy child is called a changeling, and his behavior is usually odd enough for the human mother to suspect he is not her son. Such a predicament sounds hopeless, but there is a way out. If the mother does something particularly silly—trying to boil water in eggshells, perhaps, or cook a big dinner in a teacup—the changeling will laugh and say, "Well, in all the years I have lived, I have never seen anything like that before." This proves he is far too old to be a baby, and the housewife has a right to thrust him in the oven or start to throw him in the fire. If she does so, an old woman fairy will immediately appear and exchange the real baby for the changeling.

CHIN-CHIN KOBAKAMA   Japan

This tiny fairy is said to be in charge of the beautiful thick mats which cover the floors in a Japanese house. The Japanese ladies are most particular about keeping the mats clean; but if one of them—or more likely, some of her children—should be careless, the fairies will tease them until they mend their ways. The translation of the name, as nearly as possible, is "lovely little spirit wearing a skirt."

CLURICAUN   Ireland

Some say that the cluricaun is the leprechaun gone on a spree. At any rate, he resembles his Irish brother in appearance, being a little old man in antiquated dress. He has a fiery temper and is full of mischief. Sometimes he attaches himself to a human family, and for generations they cannot get rid of him or his pranks.

DRAC   France

The dracs live in caverns underneath the rivers. They are elfin folk and occasionally come out on the bank, looking like tiny people. Then again they are said to float on the surface of the water in the shape of a golden cup or a ring. If a human being reaches out and touches one, his hand will stick fast, and he will be dragged down to the dracs' kingdom and forced to serve them for seven years.

DWARF   Most of Europe

The dwarf is the size of a small child, but he has a wrinkled, leathery skin. In some countries he is supposed to be a miner, or to work with precious stones, and often lives in an underground palace; but in Switzerland, he likes farming. Swiss dwarfs have a lively, joyous disposition and are kind and generous. They drive home stray lambs and leave berries in the paths of lost children. They keep cattle and make a marvelous cheese which grows again when it is bitten. But, if anyone eats it all, it will not reappear.

ELF   Most of Europe

These tiny folk live together in large colonies, usually underground. They are clean and dainty, and they have weddings, dances and feasts, just like mortals. If you put your ear against an elf hill, you may be able to hear their music; but it is dangerous to do so, because you may be kidnaped by them. The term "elf" is also used freely to describe any kind of fairy.

FAIRY   Europe and Asia

Like the words elf and elfin, "fairy" may cover anyone having magical powers, especially those of becoming invisible and changing into other shapes. The true fairy, however, is the tiny, graceful creature with gossamer wings who dwells in fairyland. Fairies are always happy. They never grow old or sick and are generally beautiful.

FLOWER FAIRY   China

These are the fairies of the garden who appear as young girls, dressed in white or red. They dance among the flowers, spreading their fragrance. Like most of the fairy companies, they are royalists and have their own king.

GIANT   All over the world

The giants are people of enormous size and strength. They may be friendly or hostile. Although there is occasionally a wise one in the fairy tales, they are generally rather stupid, so that those who are much smaller often get the better of them.

GNOME   Most of Europe

Gnomes are closely related to dwarfs, wizened little men of the mountains. Some of them are pleasant, and others quite the opposite. Like the leprechaun and the brownie, they seem to live in a man's world. We seldom read anything about their womenfolk.

GOBLIN   Most of Europe

Most of the fairies have their good and bad characters, but the goblins, with the exception of those in France, are generally inclined to evil. They are hideous creatures with small, deformed bodies and great bulging eyes. People are wise to run away from them. The French goblin, on the other hand, is often described as a mischievous sort of brownie. He likes to ride the horses at night and tangle their manes and tails.

GREMLIN   England

The gremlin is an imp known only to the pilots of airplanes. His tricks cause them a great deal of trouble and inconvenience. Although they are tiny, most gremlins are unusually strong and have considerable knowledge of mechanics.

HOBGOBLIN   Great Britain

The hobgoblin loves a bit of fun. He is a house fairy, as his name implies, for the hob is attached to the fireplace; but he is not inclined to sweep the hearth or wash the dishes.

JINN   Arabia

The jinn are a group of creatures from the mountain of Kaf. They are often described as looking like people, but they have the power of changing into snakes or other animals and sometimes appear in a shape half wolf, half hyena. They may also make themselves invisible. They can do wonderful feats of magic which may benefit or harm mortals. Because they are related to fire, they often appear in a cloud of smoke.

KOBOLD   Germany, Switzerland

Like the British brownie, the kobold prefers to live in a house. In the old days when travel was slow and tiring, he believed in hospitality and kindness to wayfarers, and closely watched the behavior of the family with whom he lived, rewarding the good and punishing the evil. He is particularly clever about finding lost objects. At least once when people sought to escape their kobold by moving, it did no good for he moved, too.

KORRIGAN   France

When seen by moonlight this fairy appears to be a lovely lady, who spends a great deal of time combing her golden hair. She is so beautiful that no one who sees her can forget her, and yet, the moment the sun rises, she turns into an ugly hag.

LEPRECHAUN   Ireland

The leprechaun is a fairy shoemaker, a little old man with gray whiskers who always wears a red jacket with seven buttons. He is sometimes seen by day plying his trade under a tree, making the tiniest shoe you can imagine and using only the finest leather. If you can catch him, or even fix your eye upon him, you must ask him where his pot of gold is hidden, for every leprechaun has a pot of gold. But like most of his fairy cousins, he is a tricky fellow and knows a hundred ways to escape. Even if he tells you where his treasure is, you have to be unusually clever to get possession of it.

LUTIN   France

The lutin is similar to the British Puck. He assumes many forms and enjoys playing pranks. He likes to unfasten the sheepfold or open the stable door. Sometimes he appears as a little red dwarf, and sometimes as a black horse so frisky that he throws anyone who tries to ride him.

MERMAID or MERROW   All of Europe

Although we usually think of a mermaid as a girl who from the waist down has the body and tail of a fish, the old stories do not always describe her that way. Mer people are those who live at the bottom of the sea or of a lake. The ladies are quite vain and spend a great deal of time admiring themselves in small mirrors while combing their long hair. Some of them have feet, and a few have a tail which they can pull on or take off. But those who were supposed to have been caught in tide pools along the Cornish coast certainly had fishtails. That is the reason they were stranded at low tide. If a human being comes upon a mermaid in this awkward position, perhaps because she had fallen asleep as the tide was turning, she will give him a generous present in return for being put back in the sea.

MONACIELLO   Italy

This fairy is supposed to look like a miniature monk. He appears in the dead of night to poor people who are in great need, shows them where his treasure is hidden, and then vanishes.

MOSS FOLK or WOOD FOLK   Germany

These little people, about the size of dwarfs, are supposed to have bony frames and large joints so that they somewhat resemble the trees to which they are related. They are timid and humble. Sometimes they approach woodsmen or farm laborers working in a field near the woods and ask to borrow a tool or some food. They always bring good fortune to those who lend them anything.

NECK   Scandinavia

The neck is a water fairy who lives under the shelving bank of a stream. He is a great musician. He may appear as a pretty little boy with golden hair and a red cap who can sit cross-legged on the surface of a river. At other times he may look like an old, old man.

NIS or NISSE   Scandinavia

The nis or brownie of the Scandinavian countries is the height of a year-old child. He wears a gray suit and red, pointed cap. (Red is a magic color in many countries, and a red cap often appears as a valued fairy possession.) No farmhouse thrives without a nis. He helps with the work at night, and also lends a hand during the day. There is also a church nis, sometimes called a kirkegrim, who lives in the tower and makes everyone behave in church; but he does not always behave himself. One Sunday not a sound came from the big bell. The sexton climbed up to investigate and found a bundle of rags fastened around the clapper. As he untied them he heard a chuckle and saw the red cap of the nis, peeping out of his hiding place.

NIX   Scandinavia

The nix is a water fairy who can assume many forms, such as a swimming horse or a person. Sometimes he lives in a waterfall and plays melancholy music. A lady nix is called a nixie.

OGRE   Great Britain

The ogre is the worst of the giants. He is not only hideous to look at, but he also has many unpleasant habits, such as eating little boys for breakfast.

PERI   Persia, Arabia

The Peri is said to be a good fairy, and a beautiful one. She is supposed to be descended from disobedient angels and to be trying to earn the right to return to Paradise.

PISKEY, PIXIE or PIXY   England

These are the tiny fairies of Devon and Cornwall whose dancing makes the fairy rings in the grass. In Cornwall, that southwestern tip of England which sticks out like the toe of a boot into the ocean, they are called "piskies," but in the neighboring county of Devon they are the "pixies." There are hundreds of these charming little people. They have a king and queen and a full court, to say nothing of a full orchestra, for they are fond of music. Many a person in southwestern England has claimed to have seen them.

PORTUNES   Great Britain

This fairy looks like an old man about six inches high. He is therefore much smaller than the brownie whom he resembles. He wears patched and shabby clothes and is often friendly enough to lend a hand with the work. However, he also likes to play tricks and will sometimes guide a horseman into a swamp and then go off laughing.

PUCK or ROBIN GOODFELLOW   Great Britain

Puck is supposed to be the son of a fairy father, some say the fairy king himself, and a mortal mother. He ran away from home at the age of six to escape a whipping. His father's gift to him is the ability to change himself into any sort of animal, so you can imagine what fun he has playing tricks on people. After he has fooled someone, he always shouts, "Ho! Ho! Ho!"

RAKSHAS   India

The rakshas is an ogre who frequently lives in a palace and possesses great quantities of gold and jewels. He never bothers with a brush or a comb, so his hair is long and matted. His fingernails are considered poisonous. Like all ogres, he enjoys eating people and he is usually rather stupid; but he is not always described as a giant.

RUSALKA   Russia

These water and wood maidens are something like the Greek nymphs. They have long green hair and like to swing on the trees.

SPRIGGAN   Cornwall

The spriggans are tiny creatures, so much like the piskies that they may be the same fairies under another name.

TENGU   Japan

In Japan the winged elves of the woods are called tengus. They are said to have great powers of magic and enchantment. Sometimes they resemble human beings, and sometimes birds—especially their chief who has a large, beaklike nose. He always wears a red robe and a small crown, and carries a fan made of feathers.

TOMTE Sweden

The tomte is a queer little man who behaves like the nis or brownie. He often lives in a tree close to the house he has adopted.

TROLL Scandinavia

The trolls are a strange group of beings. In some stories they are described as dwarfs. In others, they seem to be the same size as human beings; and in still others, they are giants. They hate the sun and live underground or in the depths of a dark forest. The trolls are skilled craftsmen and they are supposed to own all the riches of the mineral world. Generally they live in families and behave in many respects the way mortals do; but they all dread noise. Men have been said to drive them away by persistently ringing the church bells.

TYLWYTH TEG Wales

This is a fairy family, the size of human beings, who are not only beautiful but also courteous. They are supposed to live on an island in the center of a lake, and they have a magnificent garden. A tunnel connects their dwelling with the mainland, but it can be used only by the Tylwyth Teg. When anyone else attempts to approach their island by boat, a strong wind rises and makes it impossible for them to land.

VILA The Alps

The vila is a lady fairy who lives in the woods and in the mountains. She and her sisters are able to foretell important events and they can sometimes heal the sick. Occasionally one of them may be seen riding on a stag. If a human being does something kind for a vila, she will promise to come to his aid whenever he needs her.

WILL-O'-THE-WISP   England

If you see a tiny light moving along in front of you when you are out after dark, it may be a will-o'-the-wisp. He hopes you will follow him so that he can lead you astray. In the old days before flashlights were invented he would begin his mischief by blowing out the lanterns people carried.

WITCH   All over the world

We generally think of witches as dreadful old hags, wearing pointed black hats and riding on broomsticks; but some of them are said to be young and beautiful. The attractive ones may be just as wicked as their sisters. There are two kinds of witches, however— those who do black magic and wish to harm someone, and those who do white magic and whose spells are beneficial. Any person who practices magic may be called a witch, but the men are generally known as wizards.

Will-o'-the-Wisp

"Will-o'-the-wisp, Will-o'-the-wisp,
    Show me your lantern true!
Over the meadow and over the hill,
    Gladly I'll follow you.
Never I'll murmur nor ask to rest,
    And ever I'll be your friend,
If you'll only give me the pot of gold
    That lies at your journey's end."

Will-o'-the-wisp, Will-o'-the-wisp,
    Lighted his lantern true;
Over the meadow and over the hill,
    Away and away he flew.
And away and away went the poor little boy,
    Trudging along so bold,
And thinking of naught but the journey's end,
    And the wonderful pot of gold.

Will-o'-the-wisp, Will-o'-the-wisp,
    Flew down to a lonely swamp;
He put out his lantern and vanished away
    In the evening chill and damp.
And the poor little boy went shivering home,
    Wet and tired and cold;
He had come, alas! to his journey's end,
    But where was the pot of gold?

Laura E. Richards

Drak, the Fairy

ABOUT TWO HUNDRED YEARS AGO there lived in the little town of Gaillac in France, a young merchant named Michael. He had reached an age when he wished to settle down in life so he decided to get married. Of course he realized that he should not be too particular. Provided the girl was sweet-tempered, witty, rich, beautiful and of good family, he was willing to ignore a shortcoming or two. Unfortunately he could not see anyone in Gaillac who appeared worthy of his choice. All the young girls seemed to have some known fault, to say nothing of those which were not known.

At last he was told about a young lady of Lavaur who was endowed with innumerable good qualities and a fortune of twenty thousand crowns. This sum happened to be exactly that required by Michael to establish himself in business, so he instantly fell in love with the young lady of Lavaur. He obtained an introduction to her family, and they liked his appearance and treated him very well. However, the young heiress had so many suitors that she hesitated to make a definite choice. Her father and mother tried to help her, but they, too, were confused by the large numbers of young men, tall and short, solemn and smiling, skinny and stout. Finally they decided to give a great ball and bring all the lovers together. There they would compare them, and just at midnight they promised to announce who their daughter's future husband would be.

Michael was greatly excited as he set out for Lavaur on the day of the ball. His horse was brushed until it shone, and the bridle and saddle were polished and ornamented. Behind the saddle he strapped a portmanteau, a kind of horseman's suitcase, containing the finest new clothes: an apple green coat, a lavender vest, breeches of black velvet, silk stockings, buckled shoes and a satin ribbon to tie back his long hair. Men were fancy in their dress two hundred years ago. Furthermore, in order to keep his courage up, the prudent traveler carried a few slices of almond cake and a bottle of wine.

Now that the time had come, he was in a very anxious state; and when he saw the church tower of Lavaur in the distance, he felt quite taken aback. He pulled in his horse and began to wonder how he should behave at the ball and what he should say to the young lady. His thoughts were so disturbing that he decided to dismount and stay where he was until his plans were made. So down he sat on the turf beside the river, and in order to think more clearly he drew out the almond cake and the bottle.

As he ate and drank the sun disappeared from the horizon. Michael was about to pursue his journey when he heard a sound as of a multitude of little footsteps trampling the grass in time to a flute and cymbals. He turned around and there he saw a troop of fairies, headed by their king, Tambourinet. In their rear, turning handsprings over and over, was a little clown of a fellow called Drak.

The company surrounded Michael and gave him a thousand good wishes, and he, seeing they were so friendly, felt quite brave and welcomed them. He still had some cake left, and when he noticed that their eyes were fixed on it, he began to crumble the last slice and throw the bits to them, just as you might feed the birds. In spite of their numbers each one received a crumb except for Drak, who arrived when everybody else had finished. Then Tambourinet asked what was in the bottle, and it was passed from one to another until it reached Drak, who found it empty and threw it away.

Michael burst out laughing. "That is justice, my little man," he said to the fairy. "For those who arrive late, there remains nothing but regret."

Drak scowled at him. "I'll make you sorry for saying that," he answered angrily.

"What can you do?" asked the traveler. "Do you think you are big enough to revenge yourself?"

Drak disappeared without a reply. Michael took his leave of the company and mounted his horse again. He had not gone a hundred yards when the saddle slipped, and down he came on the ground with a great thud. He arose, feeling somewhat stunned, rebuckled the straps, and mounted once more. This time he urged his horse to a trot for it was getting late. Just ahead of him there was a bridge over the river, and right in the middle of the bridge one of his stirrups gave way. Off he went, with a great splash as he hit the water.

He waded back to shore, dripping wet, of course, and in a very bad humor; but as he attempted to mount, the whole saddle came off. The startled horse shied across the bridge, dragging Michael over the rough boards and sharp pebbles. He was badly scraped.

"Confound this saddle," he said to himself. "A pretty sight I shall look at the ball if I have no skin left on my hands and face. I shall just ride bareback and carry the saddle over my shoulder."

He managed to do so, and in this peculiar fashion he rode into Lavaur. The people who were sitting on their doorsteps to enjoy the summer evening, shouted with laughter as he came along. It is not every night that you see a rider with his hair and clothes soaking wet, and the saddle he should be sitting on, sitting on him instead.

Of course the laughter did not improve Michael's temper. "You big stupids," he growled under his breath. "I must say I see nothing funny about it."

So, in a bad frame of mind, he rode up to the inn and asked for a room where he could change his clothes. There he opened his portmanteau and began to lay everything carefully on the bed.

Now in those days men often powdered their hair, and Michael's first consideration was whether he should powder it white or yellow. Having decided that white would be best, he seized the swansdown powder puff and began on the right side of his head, looking in the mirror to be sure he was getting it thick enough. But to his amazement he noticed that the left side appeared to be coated with yellow powder without any help from him. His head looked just like a half-peeled lemon. He was now really in a hurry, and since he had always been a slow thinker, he did not stop to wonder how such a strange thing had happened. Instead, he took his comb and mixed the powder. Then he reached out for the spool on which he had carefully wound his hair ribbon.

The moment his fingers touched it, the spool rolled off the bed and across the floor. Naturally Michael went to pick it up, but it rolled away from him. Twenty times he was about to seize it, and twenty times his impatient hands missed their goal. He looked for all the world like a frolicking kitten, but altogether too big and clumsy. At last the spool rolled under a chest completely out of reach. With a sigh he gave up and put on the white ribbon he had been wearing all day.

Next, having pulled on his fine silk stockings, he stepped into his new shoes and stooped to admire them. As he did so, the right buckle fell off. He replaced it, but he had no sooner done so than the left one came loose. After three or four attempts to get both buckles on at the same time, he shrugged his shoulders and went to the bed to fetch his beautiful velvet breeches. To his amazement they suddenly jumped up and started moving about the room, just as if they were alive. Michael was petrified. He had never before known breeches to act like that. And while he stood staring at them, the vest, coat and hat joined the breeches, one above the other, exactly as if he were inside them, and away they danced, up and down the room.

"They are bewitched," he said to himself and, pale with fear, he moved back against the wall. At that moment, the strange figure turned toward him, and under the cocked hat he saw the mischievous face of Drak, the fairy.

"So it's you, is it?" cried Michael. "I'll make you repent of your insolence. Give me back my clothes instantly."

He sprang forward, but Drak merely made a face at him and ran to the other side of the room. Michael was beside himself with anger and impatience. Once again he made a rush at the fairy, but Drak dropped to the floor and dodged between Michael's legs, dragging the clothes along. Out to the staircase he ran, and after him went the young man, up four steep flights of stairs. In the garret at the top of the house they chased round and round, over the trunks and under the rafters, until with a shout of glee Drak sprang out of the attic window to the roof.

The houses of the town were close together with steep pointed roofs like a tiny chain of mountain peaks, and from one to another the chase went on. Drak leaped ahead with the greatest agility, dragging the new clothes over the dirty tiles. Michael, not nearly so sure-footed, scrambled along behind, sometimes upright, but more often on his hands and knees. At last, after a couple of hours, Drak gained the top of a high chimney where Michael was unable to follow.

Then the fairy leaned over and called out, "My good

friend, you have forced me to spoil your ball dress. But don't worry. At the bottom of this chimney I see the copper kettle of a laundress where everything can be put right." With these words Drak shook the velvet breeches over the chimney pot.

"What are you doing?" cried Michael.

"I am sending them to the wash," replied the fairy, and casually dropped the breeches into the smoking hole. Next followed the vest, the coat and the hat.

Michael sat down upon the steep roof with a cry of anguish. All his hopes seemed to have vanished. But he was a man of spirit and once again he sprang to his feet. "I shall go to the ball just the same," said he. "I'll go in my traveling clothes."

"Hark," interrupted the fairy.

The sound of a bell rang out from a neighboring steeple. Michael began to count the slow, even strokes. There were twelve of them. It was midnight, the very moment when, in the ballroom, the parents of the young lady were announcing their daughter's future husband. He wrung his hands in despair.

"What an unlucky fellow I am!" he groaned. "If I go now, it will all be over. She and her parents will laugh at me."

"And that would be justice, my big man," replied Drak, with a sneer. "You have said yourself, *'For those who arrive late, there remains nothing but regret.'* Another time, don't be so hasty in laughing at the feeble, for even the smallest may have wit enough to avenge himself."

· 30 ·

The Piskey Revelers

ONCE UPON A TIME a Cornish youth was engaged to marry a Cornish maid, and he went to see her almost every evening when his day's work was done. The name of the youth was Benet Chegwidden and the maid's, Jenefer Kellaway. Benet lived at Porteath, a farm not far from the great headland of Pentire and within walking distance of Portquin, a beautiful little cove on the north coast of Cornwall where Jenefer lived.

The youth was a farm laborer and the maid, the daughter of one. He was tall and dark and a giant for strength, and she was small and fair. Her hair was the color of gorse blossom, and her eyes were the limpid brown of the stream that ran through the Trevigo Valley.

The Kellaways' cottage faced the sea and near it ran the stream. It was a small cottage with a thatched roof, and its windows were filled with glass as green as the water that ran under the cliffs at the flow of the tide. Pale green though they were, the windows glowed like fire when the evening sun shone upon them, making it look as if it were setting behind them instead of over the sea. Within the cottage were open beams, a wide hearth, and a railed stairway leading to the bedchamber above. There was a settle, a small square table, a long bench, several fiddleback chairs and an oak dresser. On the dresser stood an ancient pint measure which had belonged to Kitty Thorn, Jenefer's great grandmother.

It was a queer old pint and had some mysterious connection with the Little People who visited the cottage every evening, so it was said. It seemed to know when its friends were waiting outside for it began to tap, tap, tap on the dresser. The Kellaways understood the meaning of these tappings, for the minute the pint began to knock Mrs. Kellaway would say, "The Little People have come, 'tis time for us to go upstairs," and no matter what time it was, or what they were doing, they climbed the railed stairway and never came down again till the morning.

The Kellaways did not mind being sent upstairs in this odd fashion, partly because they stood in some awe of the old pint measure, and partly because they did not want to prevent the Little People from coming to their cottage as they had been wont to do since the time of the great storm.

There is a tradition in the parish that Portquin was once a big fishing place with many inhabitants and a large fleet. One day when the men were out fishing in the bay, a storm suddenly arose, and every boat went down in the raging sea. Not a man was left, and soon the women forsook their homes and went inland. The forsaken houses crumbled away, and all but the more strongly built fell to pieces. The

Cornish folk say that when places are forsaken by human beings the Piskeys come to live in them, taking possession of all that remains.

When the great storm was well-nigh forgotten, some farm laborers, among them the Kellaways, came to live there. They built up the walls of the houses still left standing, fitted them with thatches, windows and doors and made them habitable.

Benet Chegwidden was a frequent visitor at the Kellaways' cottage. He seldom arrived later than half past seven when the days were long, and seldom after six when they were short; but sometimes, when there was much to do on the farm, he did not get to Portquin until close on nine o'clock. He was never late if he could help it, for he wanted to be with Jenefer as long as possible, and he did not want to be sent away by the old pint measure the moment he had come.

The pint was no respecter of persons, not even of the good-looking youth who had walked all the way from Porteath. Whether Benet had come early or late, when the pint began to knock and Jenefer said to him, " 'Tis time for 'ee to go, Benet, the Little People have come," Benet took up his hat, said good night, and left.

But Benet, although he went obediently enough on most occasions, soon began to resent being dismissed in this arbitrary fashion. One evening, when he happened to arrive unusually late, the pint started tapping the moment he crossed the threshold. It made him so angry that he told Jenefer he would not be sent away the moment he came

· 33 ·

for all the Small People in Cornwall. Moreover, he declared that he had his doubts as to whether there were little bits of men and women, and he suspected that the old pint was anxious for him to be gone for some other reason.

Jenefer was greatly distressed to hear her lad talk in this way. "There be Little People," she said solemnly. "They are the ancient ones who lived in Cornwall in the days of the Druids. They came to our cottage before my great-granfer and great-granny lived here."

"And what do they come to do?" asked Benet.

"Why, to have their little frolics as they did after the storm when all the cottages belonged to them," Jenefer answered simply. "Mother and me would not like to prevent them from coming now, an' we shouldn't know when they wanted to come in if the pint didn't tell us."

"But you have never seen the Little People," persisted Benet. "I haven't nuther, an' I have looked back to see if they were outside when you and the old pint have sent me away."

" 'Tis true that I haven't seen the Little People come into our cottage nor leave it," said Jenefer, "for I have never let my curiosity get the better of me. But I have sometimes heard the sound of little music and merry laughter when I have been upstairs in my bed."

The pint began to knock again, this time more impatiently.

"You *must* go," she urged. "We can't afford to offend the Small Folk who have been so friendly with us up till now. 'Tis lucky to have little bits of men and women come to a cottage as they do to ours, and unlucky when they are driven away from it. So, Benet, you must go!"

The earnest tone of her voice and the pleading in her eyes, more than her words, made him obey her; but there was resentment in his heart and undefined doubt in his mind as he went on his way to Porteath.

"If there be Little People who come into houses after sundown, I hope I shall see them some day," Benet muttered to himself. "I've heard the old grannie-women say that people get Piskey-eyed and may such be my good fortune, for I'm not a-going to believe what I cannot see no matter how many pint measures give me their orders."

It was the fall of the year now and the days shut in early, but Benet had much to do and often did not finish his work till late. One evening he wondered if it would be worth his while to go to Portquin, for if he got to the Kellaways' cottage when the old pint measure began to tap he would see Jenefer for scarcely more than a minute.

"But I'll just go round the cliffs all the same," Benet thought, "the walk will do me no harm."

The moon was full and hung like a hurler's ball in the cloudless sky, which was a deep, dark blue like the mussels that cling to the rocks on the shore. The sea beneath the moon was glistering with light, and the water between Pentire and an island called The Mouls was a silver fire.

" 'Tis a quiet evening," said the youth to himself, "I can hear the waves rushing into the caverns an' breaking on the beaches as plain as if I was down there."

He turned his back on Pentire and went toward Portquin, singing an old Cornish song, and as he sang his strong voice mingled with the thunder of the breakers over the smooth sand below the cliffs on which he walked. He came to a place known as Moon's Ground and suddenly stopped his singing, thinking he heard on the cliff side of him thin, gay laughter. He looked around but saw nothing that could have caused it.

" 'Twas a herring gull laughing in his sleep," Benet said.

Moon's Ground was a beautiful spot in the daytime with its heather and gorse and golden samphire, but it was weird enough after sunset. The place was full of dark green mounds called Piskey dwellings by the old people, and tiny roads soft as velvet that ran all the way to Tintagel.

Benet looked around him uneasily, then started on his way. He had gone only a few steps before he stopped again, this time at the sight of a coach about the size of a large turnip, coming out of one of the mounds and going like the wind in the direction of Portquin. It came out of the mound quietly and rolled away even more quietly, so that a moment after it was gone Benet could not be sure whether he had seen anything at all. He went on his way till he reached Trevan Point where seabirds had their dwellings in the cliffs. Benet had often heard them laughing and whistling. This evening, however, his ears were greeted by other sounds—rolling wheels and squeaky voices. He looked about him to find the cause of the sounds and thought he saw shadowy forms low on the ground, each one carrying a tiny light.

Benet was brave enough, but the sight made him feel

distinctly nervous. All the tales he had heard about the Little People came back to him as the mysterious lights bobbed to and fro. He quite forgot that only a little while ago he had told Jenefer he did not believe there were such things as dinky men and women. He even forgot he had said that if there were such creatures he would like to see them. Then suddenly it flashed across his mind that he had become Piskey-eyed.

"I don't want to see them after all," he said to himself. "I'll go back from the cliffs out of their way."

Leaving the cliffs he went over a small common and soon came to a steep hill; but he had not gone far when, to his dismay, he saw a long string of tiny coaches slowly descending the hill in front of him. They were like the coach he thought he had seen coming out of the mound, only as these were going slowly he could see them more distinctly.

They were beautiful coaches, each a different color, and drawn by horses no bigger than an eight-weeks' kitten. Behind every coach stood a man in a red coat, green hat and breeches, and red stockings, while a man similarly dressed sat on the box seat driving.

"My dear senses!" Benet exclaimed, rubbing his eyes to make sure he saw aright, "I've heard my old Granny Chegwidden say that the Little People drove about in coaches, but I didn't believe it before, no fy I didn't! And I didn't believe there was such little bits of men and women, but I believe it now!"

He had hardly said this when out from the hedge, which lay in shadow, sprang an odd-looking person about five inches tall, wearing a pointed cap. He had immense ears, a thin sharp face and no neck to speak of, and his body and legs seemed too small for his ears. The sight of this weird man so startled Benet that he backed into the opposite hedge just as a tiny coach and four prancing, white horses in green trappings passed on its way down the hill. As it went by, Benet saw two lovely faces looking out of the window.

The coach had no sooner rolled by than dozens of others passed. The last one was a golden coach-and-six with scarlet trappings like a State coach. The driver and the footman were clad in scarlet and gold, but Benet did not see the little people inside because they were not looking out. Behind this came a crowd of men and women on foot, talking and laughing one to another, their voices round and sweet like the chirps of geese-chicks soon after they come out of the shell.

These were followed by a company of musicians, fiddlers with their fiddles, flautists with their flutes, reed players with their reeds, horn players with their horns. Benet hardly breathed till this crowd had passed. When it had reached the bottom of the hill, he took off his hobnailed boots and walked down the road in his stockings.

"I must see where the Little People be going," he said to himself, "for they're going to hold a revel somewhere, 'tis plain as a weathercock. Surely they can't be going to hold it in the cottage where my dear little maid do live; there are too many o' mun for that."

He saw the coaches going over a rustic bridge which

spanned the stream. The moon was flooding the place with radiance, making everything visible. When the last of the coaches was over and the last musician had crossed, he came and stood by the brink of the stream to see where they were going. Up to the door of the Kellaways' cottage rolled the long line of dinky coaches. Then the gentlemen began helping the ladies out, and the elegant way they did it was past believing.

"And every one o' mun dressed up to the nines in velvet and silks," Benet commented admiringly. "An' as for the little ladies, they be that handsome I don't wonder the gentlemen like to bow and scrape before them as they be doing, no fy I don't!"

Each gentleman led his lady to the cottage door and disappeared; but how, Benet did not know for the door was shut. When the coaches were empty, the coachmen flicked their whips and drove up the valley and were lost in the shadow of the trees. Then the Little People who had come on foot went into the cottage, and as Benet looked closer he saw the fiddlers roll themselves as small as marbles and roll under the doorway, the flute players climb up the side-posts of the door and go through the keyhole, until there was not a dinky body to be seen anywhere.

"I wonder if I may make so bold as to peep in at the window an' see what the Little People be upon?" thought Benet. "I don't suppose the little dears will mind my looking through the window at all since I was fortunate enough to see them coming down Doyden Hill."

He stood by the window, his eyes glued to its small green

panes. For a while he saw nothing, then gradually he became aware that the room was lit with a soft light and that sounds of music filled his ear. Then he saw hundreds of Little People standing around the room, each gentleman with his lady, watching about a hundred others dancing. At one end of the room, facing the window, were two people sitting on a low footstool. They were dressed in robes that sparkled like dewdrops on gossamer, and on their heads were crowns which glittered still brighter than their robes.

"The King and Queen of the Little People, I suppose," Benet murmured. "Wouldn't Jenefer open her pretty brown eyes wide if she knew there was royalty in her father's and mother's cottage?"

Benet could hardly take his eyes from the grand little bodies on the stool; but when he could he watched the dancers, who seemed to be doing some intricate dance for they went in and out and round about till his head began to swim. To prevent himself from getting dizzy, Benet turned his gaze to the gentlemen and their ladies standing around the room. And he, who had never failed to show Jenefer those little attentions every girl expects, was delighted to see what attention the dinky gentlemen were paying their ladies.

"I don't believe our Squire could pay his lady more attention than these little bits of gentlemen be paying these tiny ladies," thought Benet.

While the lad was watching every movement of the dancing folk, a queer tapping came from the dresser.

Benet turned and saw that the old pint measure was dancing for all it was worth, knocking out the tune the musicians were playing. How the pint was footing it, Benet could not tell, as it had no feet that he could see. Up and down the dresser it went, twisting and twirling like the dancers on the floor below. As it turned, Benet saw on the smooth surface under its spout a weird face with a wink in its eye and a broad grin on its mouth, something like the face of the odd-looking man who had jumped out of the hedge when Benet was coming down Doyden Hill.

"I believe the old thing is a Piskey turned into a pint measure," cried Benet, forgetful of how he had once felt toward the pint.

"Dance a little faster, booby," called a shrill voice.

Benet saw that the little musickers were now all standing on the dresser shelves, except for some three or four fiddlers who were sitting on the edge of the top shelf with their legs dangling, fiddling away as hard as they could. The small players, for not one was over six inches tall, were playing with all their might, making faces as they played. One stood fiddling away with his head on one side, his little stumjack thrust out and his bit of a foot beating time.

"A Christmas play is nothing to it," said Benet. "However did the dinkies learn to play like that, I wonder."

Little People, like human beings, cannot go on dancing forever, and those in the Kellaways' cottage suddenly stopped, and so did the pint measure. The musicians ceased to play, and Benet half expected the old pint would return to its usual stolidness after the dancing was over, but it did nothing of the kind. Coming to the edge of the dresser, it bent over, and as it did so, one of the little ladies came over and talked to it. What she said Benet could not hear, though her words must have pleased the pint for it seemed to shake with laughter and grow visibly brighter till it glowed like a warming pan in the light of the fire.

"That old pint is a proper old flint," laughed the lad.

Most of the Little People were now sitting on the floor, which was covered with something soft and green. Small men that looked like waiters were carrying around trays laden with hedge fruit and cakes. Most of the folk were holding glasses no bigger than moss cups, and the plates in their laps were the size of the smallest daisies.

As the large company of Little People were eating and drinking, talking and laughing, the fiddlers and the other musicians began to play again. It was not dance music this time but soft music that made Benet think of faraway bells and the dripping of water, notes of young birds and the sighing of wind among the elders out on the moor. The tiny voices and silvery laughter of the folk as they feasted seemed a part of the music, and Benet felt as if he could have listened forever.

Then, after how long Benet never knew, the King gave a sign. The Little People rose from the floor. The musicians put away their instruments. The rolling wheels of the coaches could be heard. The merrymaking was over and the guests were going home. Benet clung to the sight of them until the last one had disappeared up the curves of Doyden Hill, then he turned around for one more glimpse of the room that had seen such gaiety.

The moon was coming into the cottage in a long beam of

silver, and the sight that met the lad's eye filled him with dismay. For the spry old pint was not on the dresser shelf, not on the table, but lying forlornly on its side on the hard stone floor.

"Poor fellow, perhaps 'ee had too good a time," sighed Benet sympathetically. "Whatever will my Jenefer think when she sees 'ee so?"

With no more noise than the moon made as it entered the cottage, he pushed the door open and stole softly across the floor. He picked up the old pint, brushed it off, fondled it tenderly, then put it in its place upon the shelf. Before shutting the door of the cottage, Benet looked back at the pint. The moon was full on it, burnishing its surface, and just for a moment the pint smiled back at the youth as broadly and merrily as when it had been footing it up and down the dresser.

Benet crossed the bridge quickly and went up the hill with long strides, but by the time he reached Porteath the moon had set and the morning star was rising.

The next night when Benet called on Jenefer, and all the other nights until they were married and went to live in their own cottage, he stayed as long as he had a mind to, for it was only after he had closed the door behind him that the tapping of the old pint measure gave the signal for the nightly gathering of the Little People.

By Enys Tregarthen from the collection Piskey Folk *by Elizabeth Yates (John Day Co.)*

The Blind Man, the Deaf Man and
the Donkey

A BLIND MAN and a deaf man once entered into partnership. The deaf man was to see for the blind man, and the blind man was to hear for the deaf man.

One day they went for a walk in the jungle and there they found a donkey and a huge chattee, an enormous cauldron which could be used for boiling clothes.

The deaf man said to the blind man: "Brother, here are a donkey and a great big chattee with nobody to own them. Let us take them with us—they may be useful some day."

"Very well," said the blind man, and nodded his head so that the deaf man could understand him, for in their companionship they had devised ways of making signs.

They went on their way taking the donkey and the chattee with them. A little farther along they came upon an ants' nest, and the deaf man said, "Here are some fine black ants, much larger than any I ever saw before. Let us take some of them home to show our friends."

Again the blind man nodded. "What a good present a fine black ant would make!" he said.

The deaf man took out a silver snuff box and put four or five of the finest black ants into it; which done, they continued their journey. But before they had gone far a terrible storm came on. It thundered and lightened and rained and blew with such fury that it seemed as if the whole heavens and earth were at war.

"Oh dear, oh dear," cried the deaf man. "How dreadful this lightning is! We must get to some place of shelter."

"I don't think that the lightning is bad at all," said the blind man, "but the thunder is very terrible. We had better seek some place of shelter."

Not far off was a lofty building which looked like a temple. The deaf man saw it, and having reached the place, he led the blind man in with the donkey and chattee as well, and shut and barred the door. However, this building was no temple at all but the house of a Rakshas, a fearful-looking creature very like an ogre but not so big. The deaf man had hardly fastened the door when the Rakshas came home and heard people moving about inside his house.

"Ho! Ho!" said he to himself. "Some men have got in here. I shall soon make mincemeat out of them."

He pounded on the door with his fists and called out. "Let me into my house this minute, you wretches."

The deaf man was peeping through a chink in the wall, and when he saw how hideous the creature was, he became so frightened he did not know what to do. But the blind man was very brave and he shouted, "What do you mean by battering at the door at this time of night?"

"I'm a Rakshas," answered the Rakshas angrily, "and this is my house. Let me in or I'll kill you."

The deaf man was still shivering and shaking, but the blind man was braver than ever, because he couldn't see, so he called, "Oh, you're a Rakshas, are you? Well, if you're Rakshas, I'm Bakshas; and Bakshas is as good as Rakshas."

"Bakshas," repeated the Rakshas, who was not very bright, "Bakshas, Bakshas, I never heard of a Bakshas."

"Go away," replied the blind man, "and don't you dare to make any further disturbance lest I punish you. For know that I am Bakshas, and Bakshas is the father of Rakshas."

"My father?" cried the Rakshas. "Heavens and earth! I never heard such an extraordinary thing in my life. You, my father, and in there! I never knew my father was called Bakshas."

"Yes indeed," replied the blind man. "Go away instantly, I command you, for I am your father, Bakshas."

"Very well," answered the Rakshas, for he was very much puzzled and a little frightened. "But if you are my father, let me at least see your face, for I have never seen you."

Now there was a little window high up in the wall with a table below it, so the blind man and the deaf man forced the donkey up on the table and pushed his head out of the window. It was just for an instant, but that was enough.

"Bless me," thought the Rakshas, "What a dreadful big nose my father has, to be sure!" Then he called out, "Oh, Father Bakshas, you have indeed a fearful face, but pray let me see your body as well as your face before I go away."

Then the blind man and the deaf man took the great big chattee, and while the blind man opened the door a crack, the deaf man rolled the chattee past it with a thundering

noise. Then they hastily barred the door again.

The Rakshas had been watching attentively and was very much surprised when he saw the great black thing rolling by. "In truth," he thought, "my father Bakshas has a very big body as well as a big head. He could eat me up altogether." But still he was puzzled so he cried out, "Oh Bakshas, Father Bakshas, do before I go away, let me hear you scream." He said this because all the Rakshas have a very fearful scream.

By this time the deaf man was not at all frightened, for he could tell the way things were going. When the blind man made a sign to him, he pulled out the snuff box with the black ants in it. He put one black ant in the donkey's right ear and another in the donkey's left ear, and another, and another. The ants pinched the poor donkey's ears dreadfully, and the donkey was so hurt and frightened that he began to bellow as loud as he could. "EEE . . . AUGH, EEE . . . AUGH, EEEE . . . AUGH . . . EEE"

At this terrible noise the Rakshas fled away in a great fright saying: "Enough, enough, Father Bakshas! The sound of your voice would make the most refractory obedient!"

No sooner had he gone than the deaf man took the ants out of the donkey's ears, and he and the blind man spent the rest of the night in comfort. In the morning the deaf man peered out the door to make sure the Rakshas was nowhere in the neighborhood. Then he led the blind man and the donkey back through the jungle to their own village, where they entertained everyone with the tale of their adventures.

The Lady of Tylwyth Teg

IN THE OLDEN TIME when bridges were few and far between, a ferryman would often build his cottage beside a river and earn his living by rowing people across. Sometimes they knocked at his door, or, if they were on the opposite bank, they shouted and beckoned to attract his attention. Such a ferryman used to dwell beside the river Wye in Wales. The stream there was neither wide nor very deep, and a few minutes' rowing would take him across.

One night a violent storm arose, the sort of thunderstorm that is not uncommon in the mountains. The darkness was so black that old Evan, the ferryman, could see nothing beyond his doorstep except when a flash of lightning showed up the river and the wild, wooded hills as bright as day. He put more wood on the fire and sat close to it, for an old man feels the dampness in his very bones.

As he watched the flames licking around the logs, he heard a sound, a single tap at his door. "Probably a stick blown against it," thought Evan, and he sat where he was.

Once again the tap came, and then again, louder and more insistent. "Can anyone be out in such a storm as this?" asked Evan aloud. "It's past eleven o'clock."

"Yes, yes," called a voice, and he was amazed at its gentleness. "I must cross the river. I must get to the other side before midnight. Please hurry."

Evan went to the door and opened it. On the threshold stood a woman so wrapped in cloak and hood that he could hardly see her face.

"What madness is this?" he asked. "I would take no one across the Wye tonight. Hark to the sound of it."

"Please, oh please," begged the woman, "for the need is urgent. I will pay you twice the fare."

"Twice," repeated the old man. "I would not go tonight for ten crowns of gold."

"Alas, I have no gold," said the woman, "just the one silver coin. But that, and even my purse I would gladly give you. Have courage and be kind. I must get there by midnight."

"Come in and rest by my fire," Evan replied. "The storm will be over before morning. Why should I risk my life by going now?"

"Your life! Is what is left of it so very dear to you?" asked the woman. "I am risking what I love most." And opening her cloak, she showed him that she was carrying a tiny child. "Do you think I would take a chance like this if it were possible to do otherwise? I *must* go." She turned toward the shore as if she were determined to wade into the torrent.

"Stay," cried Evan. He pulled on a coat, picked up his oars and followed her.

The river was wild, and it was all he could do to launch the boat and get his passengers and himself on board. He dipped his oars deep and strove against the current. Down stream and down stream they were carried, and he thought of the rocks and the waterfalls beyond, and pulled with all his might. In spite of his age, his muscles were strong, and at last the boat reached the other shore. As he felt it grate on the sand, there was a flash of lightning, and Evan saw the woman's purse on the seat beside him. He quickly picked it up and tossed it into her lap, saying, "Keep this, for I would not take your last coin."

She thanked him kindly, and he helped her to the shore. As she hurried off, he got back into the boat and found himself sitting on the purse. What could this mean? He was certain she had caught it. In the dark she had perhaps dropped it again. He jumped up and ran after the woman until he caught up with her.

"Your purse," he panted, "truly I want no payment."

She put out her hand from under the cloak, and as he pressed the purse into it he noticed that it was soft and smooth, not like the hands of the poor women he knew.

Back he went to his boat. The church bells were ringing twelve when he pushed out into the river, and although the storm was less violent now, the waters of the Wye still rushed wildly along so that it was hard to battle against them. It was a long while before he reached his own shore,

· 53 ·

and as he wearily shipped his oars, he happened to rest one hand on the seat. There again was the purse.

You may be sure he treasured it for the rest of his life. Often he showed it to his friends, a beautiful silk purse all embroidered with flowers of many colors, and he told his tale of rowing a fairy, without doubt the very lady of Tylwyth Teg, across the Wye.

"And the great wonder of it is this," he used to say at the end of his tale. "As often as I have been in need, I have spent that silver coin, and as often as I have opened the purse, it has always been there again."

The Fairy Shoemaker

Little Cowboy, what have you heard,
    Up on the lonely rath's green mound?
Only the plaintive yellow bird
    Sighing in sultry fields around,
Chary, chary, chary, chee-ee!—
Only the grasshopper and the bee?—
      "Tip tap, rip-rap,
      Tick-a-tack-too!
    Scarlet leather, sewn together,
      This will make a shoe.
    Left, right, pull it tight;
      Summer days are warm;
    Underground in winter,
      Laughing at the storm!"
Lay your ear close to the hill.
Do you not catch the tiny clamor,
Busy click of an elfin hammer,
Voice of the Leprechaun singing shrill
    As he merrily plies his trade?

He's a span
And a quarter in height.
Get him in sight, hold him tight,
And you're a made
Man!

You watch your cattle the summer day,
Sup on potatoes, sleep in the hay;
How would you like to roll in your carriage,
Look for a duchess's daughter in marriage?
Seize the Shoemaker—then you may!
"Big boots a-hunting,
Sandals in the hall,
White for a wedding-feast,
Pink for a ball.
This way, that way,
So we make a shoe;
Getting rich every stitch,
Tick-tack-too!"
Nine-and-ninety treasure-crocks
This keen miser-fairy hath,
Hid in mountains, woods, and rocks,
Ruin and round-tow'r, cave and rath,
And where the cormorants build;
From times of old
Guarded by him;
Each of them fill'd
Full to the brim
With gold!

I caught him at work one day, myself,
In the castle-ditch, where foxglove grows,—
A wrinkled, wizen'd, and bearded Elf,

Spectacles stuck on his pointed nose,
Silver buckles to his hose,
Leather apron—shoe in his lap—
    "Rip-rap, tip-tap,
    Tick-tack-too!
(A grasshopper on my cap!
    Away the moth flew!)
Buskins for a fairy prince,
    Brogues for his son,—
Pay me well, pay me well,
    When the job is done!"
The rogue was mine, beyond a doubt.
I stared at him; he stared at me;
"Servant, Sir!" "Humph!" says he,
    And pull'd a snuff-box out.
He took a long pinch, look'd better pleased,
    The queer little Leprechaun;
Offer'd the box with a whimsical grace,—
Pouf! he flung the dust in my face,
    And, while I sneezed,
        Was gone!

William Allingham

The Honey Feast

ONCE UPON A TIME, and a very long time ago it was, there lived beside the river Rhine in Germany a gallant knight named Osmond of Rosenberg, who took for wife a beautiful young girl called Bertha. Now Bertha was unlike many of the fine ladies of the olden days. She spoke only her own language; could not sing in Italian; never learned to read English; and knew none of the fashionable dances. But to make up for all these terrible drawbacks, she was kind and gentle and extended her hospitality to everyone. She did not travel about her vast estate in a carriage but went everywhere on foot, visiting the poor and the sick and helping them.

The praises and thanksgivings of the countryside fell upon the count and his young wife, and more than that. Golden grain grew thick in their meadows, and their vines were weighed down with juicy grapes. If ever a cloud filled with hail gathered over their castle, a magic breeze turned it swiftly away. What unseen power averted the dangerous storms? It was the kobolds in the castle.

In those days there lived in Germany a race of kindly little men who preferred to take up their abode in human habitation. They were usually friendly to people and often rewarded those who were generous and hospitable. On the other hand they hated anyone who was cruel or lazy, and visited him with all the many punishments and irritations that such small folk could inflict. Some of these kobolds had dwelt in Castle Wistgaw from time immemorial, and they naturally felt a special fondness for Osmond and Bertha.

One day as the count was walking with his wife in the gardens beside the castle, she noticed a place where the wall was crumbling, and called his attention to it. "It must be a great many years since this building has been repaired," she said. "I have seen a number of places like this, almost ready to fall in ruins. Ought you not to tear some of the walls down and build them again?"

The count was troubled. "I wish we could," he answered. "Indeed, I have often wondered what to do about it. The fact is that I am not sure it would be right to tear the building down."

"Why not?" asked Bertha.

"Well, although we have never set eyes on them, you must surely have heard tell of the good kobolds who live with us here. My father heard it from his grandfather. These little people are the very guardians of the castle. Perhaps they have grown so used to their old home as it is that if we remove parts of it and change it, they will be angry and cease to watch over the welfare of the family. Then our good luck would go with them."

His wife agreed that it would be a great mistake to drive the kobolds away, and so they decided to make the best of it and continue to live in the castle as it was.

But that very night as they lay in their enormous bedstead with its high twisted columns, the count heard a sound, the patter of little feet outside their room. The next moment, the heavy oaken door was pushed open, and in came several tiny men, dressed in the fashion of their time. They wore capes over tightly fitting coats, hose of two colors and little shoes with long, pointed toes. Their leader, whose white beard reached nearly to his waist, stepped up to the bedstead, bowed low, and spoke to the count.

"My good friend," he began in a high-pitched voice, "the news has just reached our ears that you feel the need to rebuild the home of your ancestors. We, too, have noticed the crumbling walls. In fact, we have inspected the castle closely and found that age has weakened its very foundations. Therefore we urge you not to hesitate at all, but to begin the rebuilding as soon as possible."

Count Osmond was so much amazed by what he saw and heard that he could find no words to make a proper reply. However, he raised his hand in a friendly gesture, and the kobolds took this to be a sign of agreement. They bowed again and withdrew, shutting the door behind them; but for a long time Osmond and Bertha lay awake, talking about what had happened.

The very next morning the count gave orders that the work of rebuilding was to begin, and he and his family moved into a farmhouse on their estate. A large number of workmen were employed, some to tear down the unsafe parts of the castle, others to cut great oaks in the forest for the new beams or to bring fresh stone from the quarries to strengthen the walls. The work went forward rapidly considering what an enormous task it was. In fact, it went so rapidly that some of the men were disturbed about it, and one morning they came to see the count in the greatest excitement.

"Something very strange is going on, my lord," said one of them. "The castle seems to be rebuilding itself."

The count laughed and asked him why he thought so.

"We have suspected it for several days," the workman replied, "so last night we marked the stones which were on top, and sure enough, this morning we found that others had been laid on them, and very well fitted, too."

Then Osmond guessed what had happened. The kobolds, anxious to get some sort of roof over their heads before winter came, were helping with the work. Even in those days such a tale sounded odd to the workmen; but one morning when one of them climbed the scaffolding, what should he see but a tiny wheelbarrow, not much bigger than a man's hand. It was beautifully made of ebony and bound with silver, so that it looked like a toy fit for a king.

The man who found it showed it to his companions, and that evening took it home with him as a gift for his little boy. He carried it into the house and laid it down. But before he had a chance to give it to the child, it spun itself around and out the door it went. It trundled along so fast that although the man ran after it as quickly as he could it was out of sight in a moment. At the same time he heard shrill, mocking laughter all around. The kobolds were making fun of him.

On the whole, however, the little people were kindly and good-humored, and if they had not done a fair share of the work, the castle might have been twice as long a-building. Even as it was, the work went on for three years, and although in the third summer the castle took its final shape, it was still far from finished.

Seeing this, the countess called the men together one day and spoke to them. "My good friends," she said, "you have built a beautiful home for us, and my family and I are anxious to move into it as soon as possible. The farmhouse is much too small for us, and we are not comfortable there. Let me make you a promise. If you will work faster and get done before another winter sets in, I shall give you such a honey feast as you have never known in all your days. What's more, I will take a vow that each year you, your children and your children's children shall receive this same gift from me and mine from this time on."

Now the men well knew the meaning of a honey feast, and it was not an offer to be scorned. It was a tremendous banquet which took its name from the dessert, made with honey. The promise set the mouths of the workmen watering. They redoubled their efforts and got on so well that on the first of October one of them was able to lay a bouquet

on the topmost tower, which was the customary way of showing that the work was finished.

Of course the Countess Bertha kept her promise. She caused such a feast to be prepared that it was talked about for miles around. It had to be served in the open air because there were such great numbers of guests. First the soup was brought out, but that was only the beginning. One elaborate course followed another, fish and roasts of meat and fancy breads such as you have never dreamed of, ending up with the famous honey broth. Everyone was very happy and the weather was very fine, except that just as the dessert was served a few flakes of snow began to fall. This made the countess feel that perhaps October was not the best time to hold such a celebration outdoors, and she announced that every year in the future the feast would be given in May.

So anxious was she that the custom should go on forever that she had a document written on parchment, telling her promise, and pledging that when she and the count were no longer alive the future owners of the castle should give this feast, and that every tenant and every villager, to the very poorest, should be invited to come.

She was as good as her word, and so was her son. For many years they presided over the annual banquet. But at last the castle fell into other hands.

The new owner was a harsh cruel man. When he was told about the old custom, he gave a shout of laughter. "I am not here to nourish the poor," he said, "they may dine where they please, but it won't be with me."

On the first of May he ate his dinner greedily all by himself. Then he went to bed and soon fell asleep. In the middle of the night he woke up, cold with fear, although he had no notion what had frightened him. As he lay trembling, a pale blue light came into the room, and he could see a hand stretched toward him. It held the parchment on which Bertha's promise had been written. He saw it quite clearly, and then it vanished as suddenly as it had come.

Now however great our fears may be in the night, they seem rather foolish in the morning; and the new owner of the castle, who had been a general in the army, was not a timid man. He made up his mind to give a feast that very day, but it was not to be the honey feast. Indeed not. He invited some of his rich friends and neighbors, and they were to eat in the banquet hall of the castle.

All went well until the general took his place at the head of the table. Then his face flushed with anger, for, instead of a beautiful plate with the delicious food he had ordered, all he had before him was a bit of black bread.

"Who has played this trick?" he asked his servants, for he could see that everyone else at the table had been served bountifully. "Take it away."

The steward tried to remove the black bread, but it seemed to be glued to the table. "I can't lift it, sir," he said.

Then the general tried to move it, but he was not strong enough. "Bring me something else," he commanded.

The servants were anxious to obey him, but whatever they served was changed by unseen hands into black bread. When the general moved to another place at the table, the bread followed him, and the man who took his place found a delicious dinner set before him. There was nothing for the general to do but sit back and pretend he had no appetite; but his guests felt quite uncomfortable and the banquet was not a pleasant one. On the following morning the general announced that he had received orders from the emperor to move to another castle, and he departed very quickly.

The steward had hardly seen the last of him when he opened a cupboard and came across a bag of money, which he was certain had not been there the day before. To it was fastened a tag with the words FOR THE HONEY FEAST printed clearly upon it. Now this was the same steward who had looked after the castle while Bertha's son lived there, so he knew exactly what was expected of him. He prepared the great meal just as it had always been, and the villagers enjoyed it just as much, even though it was a few days late.

Future owners of the castle, having been warned that the place was bewitched, saw to it that the promise of the countess was kept; but there was one man who thought he might save a great deal of money by simplifying the feast. He invited everyone, but he served them an ordinary dinner, ending as usual with the honey broth. The villagers accepted the change willingly because they thought the new count was probably short of money; but the kobolds knew better. They made such a frightful hullabaloo after the feast was over that not a soul in the castle could sleep all night long.

However, the loss of one night's sleep is not such a dreadful hardship, and the new count was a very thrifty man. The following year he thought of a way to save still more money. He decided to omit the dinner altogether and serve only the honey broth. What if it did annoy the kobolds? Surely the economy was worth all the trouble he might have with them.

This time the midnight visitors showed their temper in real earnest. All through the night there was a fiendish commotion in and outside the castle. Windows were broken, china was smashed, and many of the beautiful hangings and furnishings were destroyed. When the cost of all the damage was reckoned up, it came to exactly the amount which in former years had been spent on the honey feast. So, by one means or another, the kobolds got their way, and the will of the old countess was carried out. From that time on, as long as the castle remained standing, the villagers and their children and their children's children had a generous feast on the first of May.

Adapted from LA BOUILLIE DE LA COMTESSE BERTHE *by Alexandre Dumas*

Chin-Chin Kobakama

THERE WAS ONCE a little Japanese girl named Kiyoko, who was very pretty, but also very lazy. Her parents had many servants, and these servants were so fond of the little girl that they did everything for her which she ought to have done for herself. They brushed her hair and washed her face. They put on her kimono and tied her sash. They even knelt down and put her feet into her slippers. Perhaps that was what made her so lazy.

When she grew to be a young lady, Kiyoko was prettier than ever. The servants still dressed and undressed her, and did everything she asked—and she asked a great deal; but she looked so charming that no one thought much about her laziness.

Then one day she was married to a soldier. He was a fine, brave fellow, and Kiyoko admired him very much and wanted to please him. He took her to live at his parents' house where there were only a few servants. All at once the young bride found she was expected to put on her own

· 69 ·

slippers and to brush and arrange her own hair. She even had to fold up her clothes and put them away, which was very difficult indeed. Poor Kiyoko, she felt quite sorry for herself.

Since her husband was in the army, he often had to be away from home for weeks at a time. Of course, Kiyoko still had to dress herself during his absence, but she could be as lazy and careless as she wished about the house because his father and mother were so old and so kind, they never could bear to scold her.

One night while he was away, she was awakened suddenly at the hour of the ox. Now in old Japan the hour of the ox was about two o'clock in the morning, a time that is far better for sleeping than waking. Kiyoko always kept a lantern burning in her room, and by its light she could see hundreds of tiny men, no taller than her finger. They were dressed like Japanese soldiers on holiday in long robes with square shoulders, and each one wore two tiny swords. Their black hair was fastened on top of their heads in knots.

As she lay there, trembling with fright, they all began to dance round and round the mat on which she was lying, and to sing this song to her.

> Chin-chin Kobakama,
>   Yomo fuké sōro—
> Oshizumare, Hime-gimi—
>   Ya ton ton!

It means *We are the Chin-chin Kobakama; the hour is late; sleep, honorable, noble darling!*

The words seemed polite, but Kiyoko saw that the little men were really making fun of her. They laughed and made faces and then began the song again, singing it over and over. She tried to catch a few to punish them, but they jumped through her fingers like quicksilver and she could not close her hand on one. Then she tried to drive them away, but nothing she did or said had the least effect on them. They came closer and closer, leaping over her head when she lay back, pulling her hair, and tormenting her. She was sure they were wicked fairies and she was terribly afraid of them, but when morning came and they suddenly disappeared, she did not like to tell anyone what had happened. After all, she was a soldier's wife, and she did not want to seem timid. Besides, who would believe her? People would say that she had had a bad dream.

Night after night the little men came and danced, always at the hour of the ox, and they continued their pranks until sunrise. Before long Kiyoko's face grew pale from lack of sleep. She was so tired and nervous that she became sick with weariness; but still the little fairies would not leave her alone.

When her husband came home he was very much disturbed to see his young wife so pale and miserable.

"Tell me what is wrong," he said. "Let me get a doctor."

At first she was ashamed to tell him because she thought he would laugh at her. But he was so kind and gentle that after a time she described to him everything that had happened.

He did not laugh at all. "What time do they come?" he asked.

"Always at the same hour," she replied, "the hour of the ox."

"Well, don't be frightened," said her husband. "There are ways of dealing with fairies. Tonight I shall hide and watch for them."

So the brave soldier hid himself behind a screen which was beside Kiyoko's bed. He waited and watched until the hour of the ox. Then, all at once, the little men came up through the mats on the floor and immediately began to dance and sing and make ugly faces. They looked like such comical little fellows that the husband could hardly keep from laughing. It was only the sight of Kiyoko's pale face and frightened eyes that kept him serious.

He had been told that nearly all the Japanese fairies and goblins are afraid of a sword made by human hands, so he drew his blade, and reaching from behind the screen threw it into the midst of them. They all leaped into the air and fell back on the floor. They had turned into—what do you think?

TOOTHPICKS!

There were no more little warriors, only a lot of old toothpicks, scattered over the matting.

The young girl had used a new toothpick after her dinner every day, and because she was too lazy to throw it away properly, she would stick it down between the mats

on the floor to get rid of it. So the little fairies who take care of the floor mats became angry with her and tormented her.

Of course her husband scolded Kiyoko, and she was so ashamed she did not know what to say. She swept up all the toothpicks and burned them, and after that she never saw the little soldiers again.

Overheard On a Salt Marsh

Nymph, nymph, what are your beads?

Green glass, goblin. Why do you stare at them?

Give them me.

         No.

Give them me. Give them me.

            No.

Then I will howl all night in the reeds,
Lie in the mud and howl for them.

Goblin, why do you love them so?
They are better than stars or water,
Better than voices of winds that sing,
Better than any man's fair daughter,
Your green glass beads on a silver ring.

Hush, I stole them out of the moon.

Give me your beads, I desire them.

                    No.

I will howl in a deep lagoon
For your green glass beads, I love them so.
Give them me. Give them.

                 No.

Harold Monro

The Giant's Stairs

ON THE ROAD between Passage and Cork there is an old mansion called Ronayne's court, and here it was that Maurice Ronayne and his wife, Margaret, kept house. They were a worthy couple and had but one son, who was called Philip after no less a person than the King of Spain. A fine boy he was with the blue eyes of his mother and the foxy hair of his father, and brighter, his parents thought, than any child of his age.

One morning Master Phil, who was then just seven years old, was missing, and no one could tell what had become of him. Servants were sent in all directions, on horseback and on foot, but they returned without any tidings of the boy. Then a large reward was offered, but the years rolled by, and Mr. and Mrs. Ronayne had no explanation of the disappearance of their son.

Now there lived at that time one Robin Kelly, a blacksmith by trade. But independent of shoeing horses, which he did to perfection, and making plow irons, he interpreted dreams for the young ladies, sang at their weddings, and was the best-natured fellow at a christening you could find half the country round.

It so happened at the dead hour of the night that Robin himself had a strange dream, and young Philip Ronayne appeared in it. Robin thought he saw the boy mounted upon a beautiful white horse, and that the child told him he had been made a page to the giant Mahon MacMahon, who had carried him off.

"The seven years, my time of service, are clean out," said he. "If you release me from the hard heart of the rock tomorrow night, I will be the making of you ever after."

"And how will I know," asked Robin, cunning enough even in his sleep, "but this is all a dream?"

"Take that," said the boy, "for a token." And the white horse struck out and gave poor Robin a kick in the forehead, so that he roared out a thousand murders and woke up. He found himself in bed, but he had the mark of the blow, the print of a horseshoe in red upon his forehead.

Now Robin was well acquainted with the Giant's Stairs. They consist of great masses of rock which rise against the cliff side like a flight of steps from very deep water. Nor are they badly suited for stairs if you have legs long enough to stride over a moderate-sized house. The belief of the country folk was that the giant MacMahon dwelt within the cliff, up whose side these stairs led.

The dream made such an impression on Robin that he determined to put its truth to the test. However, he thought one of his plow irons would be no bad companion for him, as he knew from experience it was an excellent knock-down argument. So putting one on his shoulder, off he marched to Monkstown, where his friend, Tom Clancy, lived. When Tom heard the dream, he promised to lend Robin his skiff and to help row it to the Giant's Stairs. They had supper together and some time afterward set out.

It was a beautiful still night, and the little boat glided swiftly along. The tide was in their favor, and in a short time Robin and Tom stopped under the dark shadow of the cliff. Robin looked anxiously for the entrance to the giant's palace, which, it was said, may be found by anyone seeking it at midnight; but no such entrance could he see.

"'Tis a pair of fools we are, Tom Clancy," said he, "for coming here at all on the strength of a dream."

"And whose doing is it," said Tom, "but your own?"

At the moment he spoke, they perceived a faint glim-mering of light to proceed from the cliff. It gradually in-creased until a porch, big enough for a king's palace, unfolded itself, almost on a level with the water. They pulled the skiff toward the opening, and Robin, seizing his plow iron, jumped overboard and strode boldly forward.

As he advanced through a dark passage in the rock, he heard a deep rumbling sound, as if the entrance were closing and he was being swallowed up in the cliff forever. Then, indeed, poor Robin felt afraid.

"If you were a fool for coming here," he said to himself, "what in the name of fortune are you now?" And as before, he had scarcely spoken when he saw a small light, twin-kling through the darkness of the distance. It was out of

the question to go back, so he made his way toward it, and came at last into a spacious chamber from the roof of which hung the lamp that had guided him. Several gigantic figures were seated about a stone table, as if they had been talking together, but not a word disturbed the silence. At the head of the table sat Mahon MacMahon himself, and it was he who first noticed Robin.

Starting up in haste, he roared in a voice of thunder, "What seek you?"

"I come," answered Robin, pretending to be bold though his heart was almost fainting within him. "I come to claim Philip Ronayne, whose time of service is out this night."

"And who sent you here?" asked the giant.

"'Twas of my own accord I came," said Robin.

"Then you must choose him from among my pages," said the giant, "and if you pick the wrong one, your life is forfeit. Follow me."

He led the way into a vast hall filled with lights. Along either side were rows of beautiful children, all apparently seven years old. They were dressed exactly alike, in suits of green.

"Here you are," said the giant. "You are free to take Philip Ronayne if you will. But remember, I give only one choice."

Robin was sadly perplexed. There were hundreds and hundreds of children, and after seven years he had no very clear recollection of the boy he sought. But he walked the length of the hall beside Mahon as if nothing were the matter. They had nearly reached the end when Robin, seeing that his only hope was to make friends with the giant, decided to try a few soft words upon him.

"These children have a fine, wholesome appearance," said he, "although they have been here so long, shut out from the fresh air and the blessed light of heaven. 'Tis tenderly your honor must have reared them."

"Ay," answered the giant. "That is true for you. Give me your hand, for you are, I believe, a very honest fellow for a blacksmith."

Robin did not much like the huge size of the hand that was held out to him, and therefore presented his plow iron, which the giant seized and twisted as if it had been a potato stalk. On seeing this all the children set up a shout of laughter, and in the midst of their mirth, Robin thought he heard his name called. Immediately he put his hand on the boy who, he fancied, had spoken, crying out at the same time, "Let me live or die for it, but this is young Phil Ronayne."

"It is Philip Ronayne, happy Philip Ronayne," shouted his young companions.

At the same moment the hall became dark, and crashing noises were heard; but Robin clung to the boy. The next thing he knew he was lying in the gray dawn of morning at the head of the Giant's Stairs with Philip clasped in his arms. The child was still as he had been seven years before, not an inch taller nor a day older in appearance, and he talked of things that had happened before he was carried away as if they had occurred yesterday.

You may be sure that the worthy couple at Ronayne

Court rejoiced at the return of their son, and the reward they bestowed on Robin equaled their gratitude. As for Philip, he lived to be an old man, and he was remarkable for his skill in working with brass and iron. The village folk always believed he had learned it during his seven years' apprenticeship to the giant, Mahon MacMahon.

By T. Crofton Croker from Fairy
Legends of the South of Ireland

The Troll's Invitation

In Gotland lies a high mound known by the name of Hoberg, and within it, for many years, there lived a powerful troll. He was as ugly as most of his brothers but not so large as many of them, being about the size of a small man. Nevertheless he had the phenomenal appetite for which trolls are famous. He could eat a sheep for his lunch and come back for a whole cow for supper, topping it off with a basket of peaches as well as bread and cheese. Since he provided his own food, no one had any objection to the quantity of it. In fact, the people in the neighborhood were only too happy that he confined himself to this sort of meal and did not seem inclined to stew up the baker's wife or the schoolmaster, as other trolls had been known to do.

Nils, the farmer who plowed the land around Hoberg, always treated the troll with the greatest courtesy, and was careful not to touch the mound lest his digging cause a leak in the troll's roof. Many a troll would have ignored this kindness or considered it his just right, but the old man of Hoberg was friendly with his human neighbors. He never played tricks on Nils and he sometimes gave him a net full of fresh fish, so the two got on well together. The farm prospered and Nils was a happy man.

One morning, however, the shepherd boy saw the farmer pacing up and down the barnyard with a troubled scowl on his face.

"That's a curious thing," thought the boy. "It is only a few days since my mistress had a son, her first child. This is surely a time of all others that the master should be rejoicing."

He therefore approached the farmer and asked him if anything had gone wrong. "One might think from the look on your face that the crops had failed," said the boy, whose name was Halvor, "but the farm has never been better. Do let me know whether I can help you."

The farmer was well aware that Halvor was a quick-witted lad, so he decided that it might be wise to tell him what the difficulty was. "It is true," said he, "that I should be the happiest of men, but I have a great problem. You know that the old troll of Hoberg has lived here for many years, and I have always been able to keep on good terms with him. Now we are planning a christening party for the baby, and a grand party it will be. But what about the troll? If I invite him, he will eat me out of house and home, and he may terrify my guests. On the other hand, if I do not invite him, he will be very angry. He might even bring ruin upon my farm."

Halvor was silent for a moment or two, thinking the matter over. Then he said, "You must certainly invite the troll, but in such a way that he will refuse the invitation."

"A fine idea," Nils replied, "if I knew how it could be done."

"Let me invite him," said the boy. "When I see him, I may know better what to say."

The farmer consented, and Halvor set out that afternoon to pay a visit to Hoberg. He found the troll's front door in the side of the hill and thumped boldly upon it. Immediately the troll flung it open.

"Dear me, dear me, what a racket!" he said. "A loud knock is most unpleasant to my ears."

"And surely his ears are the largest I have ever seen," thought the boy, "and his eyebrows are very bushy and fierce; but the eyes under them do not look unkind." So he spoke to the troll fearlessly.

"I am sorry my knock was so loud," said he. "My master, Nils, has sent me to bring you his greetings and to invite you to a christening party. Perhaps you have heard that he is the father of a fine baby boy."

"I had heard of it," the troll replied, "and I am pleased indeed that he has invited me. Tell him that I shall be very glad to come. No one has ever invited me to a christening before, but I have been told that they are fine affairs. I believe it is the custom to send a present to the baby."

"Most of the guests do give something," Halvor answered.

"Come in then," said the troll. "I see that you are carrying a basket and I shall put something into it."

With that he led the boy into his kitchen, a large room in the hillside, plainly furnished with oaken chairs and table like any other kitchen. From a closet at the back the troll pulled out a sack, just as you might pull out a sack of potatoes, and thrust a quart measure into it. When he drew it out, the measure was filled with gold.

Halvor's eyes opened wide in amazement as the gold was poured into his basket.

"Do you think that will be a good present?" asked the troll. "You must tell me, since I have never been invited before. Is this what people give?"

The boy wanted to do as well as possible for his master, so he answered, "That will do very well. Many give more, but some give less."

"Then I must add to it," said the troll. And once again he plunged his arm into the sack and filled the measure. "Is that better?"

"That is *much* better," Halvor replied. "Some give more, but many give less."

At that the troll scooped out so much gold that the basket was filled, and the boy realized it would be all he could do to carry it home. "Ah," said he, "I am sure none give more, and most give less."

"Good," replied the troll. "It sounds as if there might be some very important people at the christening. Who else is to be invited?"

Now Halvor knew that trolls are not fond of churchmen, so he answered, "I believe the bishop is one."

"The bishop," repeated the troll. "I am sorry to hear that. However, he is a man who carries his nose in the air. If I stay at the back, he is not likely to notice me. Who else is coming?"

Halvor thought he really must do something to prevent the troll from making his appearance, so this time he said, "I think my master is going to invite St. Peter."

"You don't mean it?" cried the troll. "I never would have thought your master had such high connections. I don't believe St. Peter and I would hit it off well at all. However, he is most unlikely to eat anything. I shall just stay in the dining room and keep out of his way."

"The dining room," thought Halvor, "that is the very place my master would like you to avoid." He wondered what on earth he could say that would discourage the old man. Then he remembered how the troll had objected to his thumping on the door, and he had a bright idea.

"My master has also planned to have very fine music," he said. "He is asking a band to come from the city, a band with six drummers."

When he heard that, the troll shook his head until his great ears flapped against it. "Oh no," he said. "No, no, that would be more than I could bear. I am dreadfully sorry, but you must please tell your master that I shall not be able to come. I should like to very much, but six drummers! You have no idea what a sound like that does to my head. It's worse than thunder and church bells. Thank him for his invitation, but really, I cannot accept it."

Halvor promised to give his master the message, and trudged back to the farm carrying his heavy burden. The farmer, you may be sure, was pleased at the way he had solved the problem and gave him a gold piece for himself.

The Little Elf

I met a little elf-man once,
  Down where the lilies blow.
I asked him why he was so small,
  And why he didn't grow.

He slightly frowned, and with his eye
  He looked me through and through.
"I'm quite as big for me," said he,
  "As you are big for you."

John Kendrick Bangs